The
Fraggles
Alphabet Pie

This book belongs to:

This 1988 Muppet Press book is published by Longmeadow Press.

Printed in Italy

h g f e d c b a

The Fraggles Alphabet Pie

by Harry Ross   illustrated by Larry Di Fiori

CHILDRENS PRESS CHOICE

A Longmeadow title selected for educational distribution

ISBN 0-516-09073-9

A picked an apple.

B baked it.

C

C carried it.

D

D drove past it.

E was excited by it.

F fought for it.

G got it.

H hollered for it.

I inspected it.

J jumped for it.

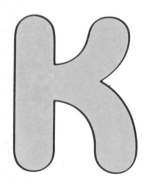

K kept it.

L lifted it.

M moved it.

N nibbled at it.

O opened it.

P peeked at it.

Q quartered it.

R reached for it.

S shared it.

T tasted it.

U upset it.

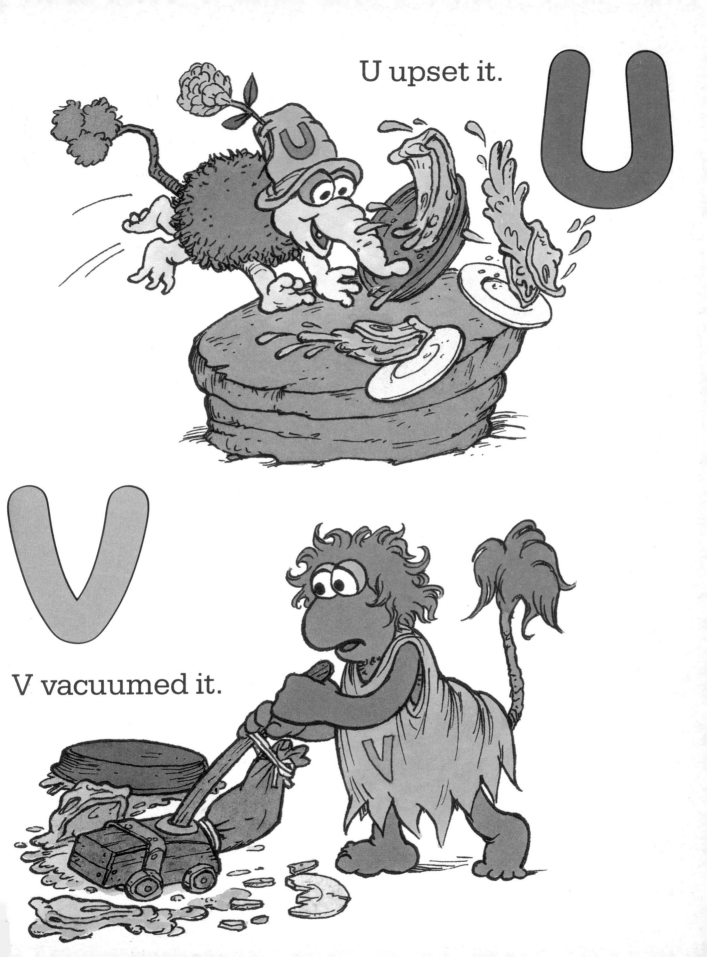

V vacuumed it.

W

W washed up after it.

X

X marked it.

Y yawned after eating it.

Z went to sleep and slept all night.